Discarded

Given to

Mrs. Waite

DEBORAH SAMPSON
Soldier of the Revolution

DEBORAH SAMPSON
Soldier of the Revolution

Harold W. Felton
Illustrated by John Martinez

DODD, MEAD & COMPANY
NEW YORK

To my wife

Library of Congress Cataloging in Publication Data

Felton, Harold W
    Deborah Sampson, soldier of the Revolution.

    Includes index.
    SUMMARY: Biography of Deborah Sampson
Gannett, a young woman who, disguised as a man,
served in the army during the American Revolution.
    1. Gannett, Deborah Sampson, 1760-1827—Juve-
nile literature.   [1. Gannett, Deborah Sampson,
1760-1827. 2. United States—History—Revolution,
1775-1783—Biography] I. Martinez, John. II. Title.
E275.G193   973.3'3'0924 [B]   76-13438
ISBN 0-396-07343-3

CONTENTS

FOREWORD

DEBORAH SAMPSON occupies a unique place in the chronicles of American women. She served as a soldier in the American Revolution.

The basic facts are well documented. They are found in public records relating to her pension for military service and in service-related papers. Many official original records were lost in 1814 when the war office was burned by British troops.

News accounts written shortly after the war supply information. So do local histories and archives. Cora Cheney's book, *The Incredible Deborah* (Scribner's, 1967) includes a detailed bibliography.

The first biography was written by Herman Mann, a literary gentleman from Dedham, Massachusetts, in 1797. The title was *The Female Review, or Memoirs of an American Young Lady.* Mr. Mann prepared his book with Deborah's assistance or, at least, with her consent. A few quotations from his preface may serve to indicate his, and her, position and purpose.

> Having critically weighed her own feelings and wishing to gratify the curiosity of many, of whom she had taken advice—with extreme *modesty* and *trembling* diffidence, she consented to take a public *Review* of the most material circumstances and events of her life. She relies on that candor and impartiality from the public, that now attend the detail of her *memoirs*. . . .

> The authorities upon which I have ventured, for the support of the facts related in the following *MEMOIRS*, are not merely the words of the lady's own mouth. They have been detailed to me by persons of veracity and notoriety, who are personally acquainted with the circumstances. . . .

> She dreads no censure—no lash of aspersion more than that of the judicious and virtuous. My own wishes are in this respect, as in all others, that truth, candor and charity may be our ruling principles.

Mr. Mann revised his book after further discussion with Deborah before his death in 1833. His son undertook a further revision which was completed in 1850. Neither has been printed, although the revision was much quoted and drawn on by Mr. John Adams Vinton, a minister from Boston, who caused the original to be reprinted with an introduction and notes in 1866. This volume, in turn, has been reprinted by Arno Press in 1972.

Another volume, written by Mrs. Elizabeth F. Ellet, contains a shorter sketch of Deborah's life. It is in *Women of the American Revolution*, published in 1818 when Deborah was still alive.

While there is no doubt of Deborah Sampson's military service, questions of some of the details of her life have been raised by Mr. Vinton, despite Mr. Mann's protestations that he had written the whole and absolute truth. Mr. Mann dates the beginning of her service in April, 1781. Mr. Vinton says it was not until May, 1782.

Deborah wrote in one pension application that the date was April, 1781. In another she gave the date as May 20, 1782. There are a number of documents that support both dates. Mrs. Ellet wrote that Deborah enlisted in 1778. Some of the subsequent writers followed her lead.

The same sort of confusion exists as to the name Deborah adopted for army purposes. In one pension application she wrote it as Robert Shurtleff. In another, she spelled it Shirtliff. Other writers, in the government and out, spell it Shurtliff, Shurtlieff, Shurtlieffe, to give a few examples just to show how muddy the water is. In Mr. Mann's book, with introduction and notes and criticism by Mr. Vinton, the name is spelled six different ways, with no comment. I have used the spelling,

Shirtliff, as Deborah did in her application for pension dated
January 11, 1792.

Anyone who has paid more than cursory attention to matters
relating to the American Revolution knows that uncertainties
are certain as to names and dates. They know, too, that tradi-
tion, custom, legend are often as important and as revealing as
the clear and positive truth as seen or heard by any one person
and written down.

None of this means that they are utterly false. It means only
that people writing them were doing their best and that they
were not very good at spelling or noting or remembering dates.
Such failings remain with us in a world that is not in the tur-
moil of creating a nation or fighting hard to win a war.

In the documents available in Deborah Sampson's case, few
can be accepted in their entirety. Often, to accept either a date
or a spelling as gospel, it is necessary to reject the other as
error. For these reasons, I have seen fit not to ignore Mrs.
Ellet in her relation of events at Medway, Massachusetts, when
Deborah used the name, Timothy Thayer. Similarly, local tradi-
tion supports the interlude at Holden, Massachusetts.

At one point in Mr. Mann's work, it is said, "From thence
(Wrentham) she visited some of the western towns of the
state." That would have covered a lot of territory. Mr. Vinton,
feeling graced with some sort of omnipotence, disputes this,
but supplies no convincing evidence to support his contrary
view. When one gets down to relating the precise events in the

life of a girl disguised as a boy in 1781 or 1782, one is, as Deborah's companions in arms might have said, "spittin' kind of thick."

At first thought there may be a tendency to doubt it, but there is no evidence that Deborah Sampson was other than feminine and virtuous. It is generally agreed that she began to assume male clothing as early as the spring of 1781, even though she may not have enlisted and entered her major period of military service until the spring of 1782.

I have undertaken to account for that year by giving credence to a visit to some of the western towns. It offers an opportunity to explain Medway and Holden. There is no reason to suppose she might not have gone back to Middleborough once in a while, thus accounting for her seeming presence there at times.

Deborah had a valuable skill as an excellent spinster, and she could sew and knit and weave as well as operate a spinning wheel. She could also do what was known as a man's work. Thus, she was financially independent and had the means to live wherever she wished.

Then, too, it seems unlikely that a girl would dress like a man and enlist without substantial preparation, at least enough preparation to give her the firm view that she could make a go of it. There were often short enlistments for specific purposes or imagined purposes. The military was no more perfect then than it is now.

All of this does no damage to the basic facts of her enlistment and her service in the army as a soldier, and it does serve to explain some otherwise unexplained statements and traditions.

These comments are made here in order to avoid the necessity to pause and undertake to justify or explain or qualify in the text.

—*Harold W. Felton*

Chapter 1

A BIRTHDAY CELEBRATION

DEBORAH SAMPSON looked across the valley. "It's a birthday celebration, that's what it is. They had a tea party for me," she said.

"No such thing. Those folks in Boston never even heard of you way down here in Middleborough. Why, Boston is nearly thirty miles away," said Jennie. "Anyway, your birthday is today and it happened yesterday. It happened on December 16."

"But I heard about it today, and today is my birthday, December 17, 1773, and I am thirteen years old. It's about time I got a really good birthday present." Deborah drew her cloak and scarf tight. The midafternoon sun was rapidly falling toward the horizon.

She felt comfortable here in the grove at Barden's Hill. An overhanging rock ledge made a shallow cave in the hillside, protected by thick hemlocks on each side. It was her secret place, shared only with Jennie.

"The Boston Tea Party! Just think of it. All those men threw tea into the bay rather than pay taxes on it," Deborah said.

"That's too much for me. I don't understand it at all. Why didn't they use it up to make tea?" asked Jennie.

"It was a protest. If Americans are not represented in the English Parliament, they shouldn't be taxed. No taxation without representation!" Deborah declared resolutely.

"You know a lot, Debbie," said Jennie with admiration

"Well, all you have to do is to read, and study, and listen," Deborah replied.

"But I'm only a slave," said Jennie.

"You are as good as anyone else," Deborah said. "I am only a servant girl, indentured until I am eighteen years old. I am sure Judge Oliver would let you learn to read and write if you would ask him."

"My mother is Judge Oliver's slave, and so am I. Slaves aren't supposed to go to school. When I can be spared, I am rented out to other people to spin or sew or clean up or work at anything they want me to do. Anyway, I'm too old to learn."

"You are not. I will teach you all I know."

"Your master, Deacon Thomas, and Mistress Thomas let you go to school," said Jennie.

"That's because they are supposed to give me a good Chris-

tian education. But I go to school only a few weeks in the summer after the hay is in and before the harvest, and in the deep of winter," Deborah said .

"But you help the Thomas children with their school work. I think you learn more than they do," Jennie said.

"I try." Deborah smiled.

"Learning is so easy for you," Jennie replied.

"No, it isn't easy. But I like it." Deborah's smile faded into a frown. "Deacon Thomas is good to me, but I'm his servant and he wants me to work. He often says to me, 'You are always hammering on some book. I wish you wouldn't spend so much time scrabbling over paper.' "

"But you keep on reading and writing anyway. I'd be scared."

"I do, yes. And I will keep on, as long as my work is done. I am thirteen years old, and I can read and write better than anyone in Deacon Thomas's family."

"Everything comes so easy to you."

"Easy? How can you say such a thing? You live with your mother, and I can't do that. I've been sent off to live with other people ever since I was five years old. That's when my father died at sea. After that, my mother couldn't support us children and we all had to go live with other people, my older brothers and my little sisters too. We were scattered to wherever a roof could be found for us. And I always had to earn my keep. There is nothing easy about it."

"Oh, Lordy, look! The sun is no more than an hour high. We have to go!" Jennie exclaimed excitedly.

Deborah didn't want to leave her secret place yet. She wanted to be alone for a while. "You go, Jennie," she said. "I will come along later."

"See you," Jennie cried. She turned and hurried down the hillside.

Deborah turned to her own thoughts and pondered on what she had just said. No, it wasn't easy.

Deborah Sampson's ancestors included William Bradford, who had been the Governor of Plymouth Colony, and Miles Standish, John Alden, and others who had governed, fought for, and developed the Massachusetts Colony. Her father was Jonathan Sampson, Jr., and her mother's maiden name was Deborah Bradford. Deborah herself was born in Plympton in Massachusetts on December 17, 1760.

Fortune did not smile on Jonathan Sampson. He failed at farming and became a sailor to support his family. He did not come home often. Then a time came when he did not come home at all. Lost at sea, they said.

Deborah's mother had to put the older children in the homes of other people where they might work for their food and shelter. At the age of five, Deborah was sent to live a few miles away with Aunt Fuller, a distant relative. Her mother was lucky to find a place as a servant in a home in Plympton where she could keep her two babies with her.

Aunt Fuller was good to Deborah. She taught her letters and numbers and the first part of the catechism. Aunt Fuller was old, her poor legs swollen and hardly able to support her heavy body. Uncle Fuller, her brother, was old too, but the pair of them ran a small farm and kept a small house.

Deborah's legs worked for Aunt Fuller. So did her hands. There was plenty for a little girl to do—the errands, the cleaning, the chickens, the garden.

As Aunt Fuller slowed down, Deborah speeded up. It lasted three years. Deborah was eight years old when Aunt Fuller moved her large body for the last time. The end was sudden.

But there was no pause for Deborah. She later said, "As I was born to be unfortunate, my sun soon clouded."

Chapter 2

DEBORAH'S APPRENTICESHIP

THE REVEREND SYLVANUS CONANT was the minister at Middleborough, a town near Plympton and only a few miles from Aunt Fuller's farmhouse. He had helped Deborah as she struggled with her catechism. He admired the bright little girl. Her spirit and her quick mind impressed him.

Deborah's mother came to Aunt Fuller's funeral. She spoke to the Reverend Conant. "What will I ever do?" Mistress Sampson asked. "There is no room for Deborah where I find my keep." Tears filled her eyes as she drew her daughter close to her.

"I will consider. For the present, take Deborah with you. You can keep her for a short time. The Lord will provide," Mr. Conant said.

At the house where her mother worked, Deborah tried to make herself as small as she could. She helped in the kitchen. She obeyed her mother and didn't cry. Perhaps no one would notice her. Then she could stay. It was so comforting to be there with her mother.

But it did not last. In three days the Reverend Mr. Conant came. "I have a place for Deborah," he said.

"Where?" Mistress Sampson asked. Deborah felt the fear in her mother's voice. A young girl's welfare depended on how her mistress treated her.

"With Madam Thacher," Mr. Conant answered.

"She lives in Middleborough."

"It is only some five miles distant from Plympton. Mistress Thacher goes to my church."

"She is old," Deborah's mother said.

"Yes, but she is in reasonably good health. And she is a God-fearing woman. She is the Reverend Thacher's widow," he added impressively.

"But her age. Can Deborah do the work?"

"I am confident she can."

"She is but a child."

"I am eight years old," Deborah said proudly. "I know I can do what is needed." She hoped to quiet the fear she sensed in her mother's words.

"It will be a good home," said the Reverend Conant. "In Middleborough I will be in constant touch."

So Deborah went to live with Mistress Thacher, a tall, thin woman who coughed and prayed. She also listened to Deborah

say her catechism and sometimes helped her with letters and numbers. The girl soon learned to read the Bible to Mistress Thacher.

Deborah was up first in the morning to start the fire and fan it into flames. She helped Mistress Thacher dress, and prepared the gruel. She was last in bed at night, after helping Mistress Thacher undress, then washing the dishes and banking the fire. And Deborah soon learned to make the modest meals the old lady needed.

In the hours between dawn and dark, there was the house to care for, the sewing and the mending. At first, Deborah helped the old lady, but as Mistress Thacher weakened, Deborah did more and more of what had to be done.

It was hard work. The hours were long. Food that was suitable for an aged woman was not right for a young and growing girl. So Deborah began to weaken too. She grew listless and pale.

Her mother seldom saw her. The Reverend Conant did not notice at first. Deborah did her work and did not complain.

Poor Mistress Thacher took to her bed more and more often, and for longer times. Some days she did not get up at all.

Gradually it became clear to Mr. Conant and to Deborah's mother that the girl must have a change. Mistress Thacher needed a much stronger person to assist her. A nurse came to the house, but in a short time Mistress Thacher faded away in death. It was 1771. The old lady was eighty-four years old. Deborah Sampson was almost eleven then.

Mr. Conant found a new place for Deborah. Deacon Benjamin Thomas, who lived on a farm two miles from Middleborough's Four Corners, needed a servant girl. Deborah was apprenticed to him until she became eighteen years old.

"Your tasks will be simple ones, tasks that become a girl," said Deacon Thomas. Deborah stiffened inside. Tasks that become a girl! Didn't he know that a girl could do anything a boy could do? She would like to tell him! She would show him!

Deacon and Mistress Thomas already had a large family, and more babies came. Care of the babies and the smaller children became one of Deborah's "simple tasks." So did helping with the cooking and cleaning, the washing, carding, spinning, weaving, sewing.

Deacon Thomas's ideas of simple tasks, well becoming a girl, included part-time care of the horses, sheep, cows, pigs, and chickens; feeding, milking, butchering, churning, buttermaking, plowing, harrowing, haying, harvesting, and some work in the forge.

But he was not unkind. The Thomases lived well. Their table was heavy with good food from their farm. Deborah soon gained weight and lost her frail, pale look.

They let her go to school when she could be spared from the farm work. It was only for a few weeks each year, but she found a way to satisfy her desire to learn. She supervised the study of the Thomas children, and she taught what she learned to the ones not yet old enough to go to school. But more often than not, when she turned to a book without a Thomas child at her elbow, the Deacon would soon find something else for her to do.

She was grateful to the Thomases and obedient, but sometimes she chafed at it all. It seemed like such a humdrum life. She longed to see the world, to experience new things, see new people.

"Oh, if I could only travel!" she often said to herself. "If I could only get away!"

Chapter 3

CLOUDS OF WAR

ONE OF THE tasks Deborah liked most was going to the Four Corners. There she delivered eggs, milk, and butter to the inn. At the inn she could see people and hear the exciting news from Boston of the conflict between the American colonies and England.

That is what she had done on December 17, 1773. On her way home she had met Jennie, and the two girls climbed up the slope of Barden's Hill to the grove and the sheltered spot Deborah called her "secret place."

She had remained too long after Jennie left, so she had to run home and was quite out of breath when she opened the door.

"I had begun to worry about you," said Mistress Thomas.

"You are late," said Deacon Thomas.

"The Deacon does like an early supper these winter afternoons. The days are so short," said Mistress Thomas.

"Can't work late in the fields," the Deacon added. "Where have you been?"

Deborah hurriedly took off her coat and scarf and hung them on the wooden peg on the wall. She began to set the table.

"Where have you been?" the Deacon insisted.

Deborah wanted to pretend she didn't hear, but she knew the Deacon would ask again. "Are you speaking to me, sir?" she asked.

"Indeed I am. I asked you where you have been."

"At the inn," said Deborah. "I delivered the eggs and butter there."

"All this time? What could you have been doing there for so long?"

"I was listening to the talk about Boston. They destroyed English tea there yesterday. The Boston Tea Party, they call it. And it happened on my birthday."

"Today is your birthday, the seventeenth of December. Yesterday was the sixteenth."

"Yes, I know, but I heard of it today, so I'll just pretend," said Deborah happily.

"Pretend?" The Deacon could not understand that.

"Oh, Benjamin, young people always pretend. Don't you remember how you did?" asked Mistress Thomas.

"I certainly do not," Deacon Thomas said firmly.

"Deborah, I have a maple cake for your birthday. And here

is a pair of mittens I knitted for you. I do wish you a most
happy birthday."

"Happy birthday!" the children cried.

"Oh, how lovely! Thank you. Thank you all, so very
much," Deborah replied.

"You should not be stopping around the inn and listening
to talk of political troubles. That is men's talk. It is not for
girls," the Deacon said.

Men's talk . . . not for girls. That is what men always said.
But they let you pitch hay and tend the animals. One thought
piled on another. But Deborah smiled at the Deacon and said,
"Yes, sir." Then she added, "But I would like to have been
there, at the Boston Tea Party."

"That's not for womenfolk," the Deacon said sharply.

"Let me help dish up, Mistress Thomas," Deborah said as
she turned toward the fireplace and the steaming pots.

The food was soon on the table and the large family seated.
The baby was at Deborah's left and one of the smaller children at her right, so that she could help them with their
meal. The other of the younger children flanked Mistress
Thomas.

"Deacon Thomas," Deborah said timidly after grace was
said.

"Yes?"

"Women in the Bible took part in political affairs, and they
even fought in wars."

"If they did, times were different then. Anyway, I don't recall . . ."

"Oh, yes. There was Deborah."

"Deborah?"

"I am named after her. My mother is too. Her story is in the Book of Judges. She was a prophetess and a judge, and she went to war."

"I don't remember."

Deborah was certain the Deacon remembered. He often forgot things he didn't want to recall. Deborah was also certain she was on safe ground. Deacon Thomas would not be likely to forbid discussion of the Bible.

"The people came to Deborah and asked her how they might become free of the oppression of Jabin, the King of Canaan, who held them in bondage. She called on Barak, the general, to go against Sisera, who was the captain of Jabin's army. But Barak said to Deborah, 'If thou wilt go with me, then I will go; but if thou wilt not go with me, then I will not go.' And Deborah said, 'I will surely go with thee.' "

"Ah, yes, I do remember," the Deacon said.

"If Deborah in the Bible did it, why is it that girls cannot go into battle now, as the boys do?" asked Deborah.

"There is no battle."

"There will be if the English continue to tax us without representation."

"My, you do learn a lot at the inn, don't you?"

"I talk to the Reverend Conant too."

"We are all Englishmen in this land. I think the present troubles may soon be settled," the Deacon said. He was saying what many Americans said and thought.

"But why must girls and women be tied down to the kitchen and the home? Why can't they . . ."

"Women do women's work. Men do men's work."

"But why is there a difference? I help in the fields. So do most women. I chop wood. I . . ."

"There is no use to talk about it," Deacon Thomas said. "It is time to do the late chores."

"But after Deborah and Barak won the battle, the land had peace for forty years."

The Deacon looked at her sternly. Deborah bit her lip. That's the way it always was. Men wouldn't talk of the things she wanted to talk about.

"Tell us more about Deborah in the Bible," one of the children cried.

"Yes, tell us," another urged.

"I think we should study your schoolbooks," Deborah said. "After the kitchen is cleaned and the night chores are done, perhaps then."

"Yes," Mistress Thomas agreed.

"Study is good up to a point," the Deacon said as he put on his heavy coat, getting ready to go to the barn to see the animals put up for the night.

"After we study, will you tell us about Deborah in the Bible?"

"If there is time," Deborah said softly. "Go get your books ready while your mother and I clear the kitchen."

Middleborough was off the main road to Boston, but post-riders, special expresses, and travelers brought the news from the city.

The town militia was increased and musters of the soldiers were held often. Deborah was at the village green, watching, whenever she could manage it. When men passed through the village, each had a tale to tell. Deborah soaked it all up like the dry earth soaks up rain during an August shower.

Each event and each date burned a place in her mind and memory. In March, 1774, the British closed the port of Boston, suppressed the Town Meeting there, and dissolved the Legislature for Massachusetts. Boston was to be punished for dumping English tea in the harbor.

On September 5, the First Continental Congress met in Philadelphia. John Adams, John Hancock, and Samuel Adams from Boston went there. The Middleborough Town Meeting appointed a Committee of Correspondence to keep in touch with what was going on in other communities.

Each year Deacon Thomas gave Deborah a few chickens, a lamb, or a piglet to raise as her own. She was supposed to do something sensible and worthwhile with the money when the animals were sold. She had planned to buy cloth for new dresses, but now she wouldn't use English cloth. Instead of spending the money, she gave it to the Middleborough committee which had been appointed to help feed the poor people of Boston, who were in great distress.

The battles of Lexington and Concord were fought on April 19, 1775, Fort Ticonderoga on May 10. Bunker Hill followed on June 17. Middleborough militia companies answered each alarm call. When they marched, with drums beating and fifes playing, Deborah's heart went with them even though she could not.

General Washington took command at the siege of Boston in early July of 1775. In March, 1776, the British fled from the city as the cannon seized at Ticonderoga began to roar. The Declaration of Independence was adopted on July 4, 1776. There was a great celebration in Middleborough, with all the church bells ringing.

Deacon Benjamin Thomas answered an alarm call and went to Roxbury with the militia in 1776 for an eight-month term. He answered other later alarms and was often away from home. Deborah's work on the farm increased.

She didn't mind working hard, but it was so dull, when there was so much going on. The American army retreated from Long Island and New York, across into New Jersey. General Washington crossed the Delaware River with his troops. The patriot Nathan Hale was executed as a spy by the British. An American army was defeated in Canada.

Word came that the British had invaded Rhode Island, only a few miles away from Middleborough. There were calls for the militia at New Bedford and Fairhaven, a short distance south, on Buzzards Bay. Men marched off to fight. Deborah Sampson watched them go, and envied them.

Chapter 4

THE FORTUNE-TELLER

"I'M SO TIRED of staying here in Middleborough, I don't think I can stand it," Deborah cried.

"Goodness sakes, Debbie. I think you're lucky." Jennie looked up from her loom.

"Lucky?" Deborah paused in her spinning. "How can you say such a thing? It's 1781. I'm twenty years old, and I never get to do anything I want to do."

"You go to all of the best houses and spin for the best people—the Sproats, the Bournes, the Clarkes, the Mortons, the Olivers, and here at the Leonards. All the rich people in town want you to work for them. Why, you will be here at Captain Benjamin Leonard's house for six weeks, maybe longer. You can work in any of the nice houses whenever you want to. And you are always welcome at the Thomases' home."

"Yes, that's true. Deacon and Mistress Thomas always invite me to come and live with them whenever I can. Of course, I help them with the work. My old room is ready for me whenever I want it. I keep the few extra clothes and my other things that I am not using there. But you go to different houses to spin too."

"But you get paid for it. Eight pence a day and keep! All I earn goes to my master, Judge Oliver. You'll have a goodly sum when you are through here."

The girls turned back to their work.

"I want to travel," Deborah said. In her heart she knew she was fortunate, but she had a feeling of unrest that seemed never to leave her.

"You do travel. And you could do more of it if you wanted to. People in other towns want you to spin for them. You are the best spinster around. You could go to more towns, and you could stay away longer."

"I have done that. But I'm still a servant, working for pennies and keep."

"And you teach school too. I bet you get a lot of money for that."

"Twelve pounds for each summer session," Deborah answered.

"And you've taught for two summer sessions."

"Yes. But the money isn't worth much because of the inflation."

"I still think you are lucky. You can teach because you learned more than anyone else. More than the Thomas children, and they went to school lots more than you did," said Jennie.

Suddenly Deborah stopped spinning and turned to her friend. "Jennie, can you keep a secret?"

"I guess so."

"Guessing isn't good enough. Can you, for certain?"

"Yes, I can."

"On your honor? Swear on the Bible?"

"Yes. All those things," Jennie declared.

"I have a suit of men's clothes," said Deborah.

"No!"

"Yes, I have. And I have worn it several times."

"You have? When? Where?"

"Once I went to Taunton. I changed my clothes in the woods, at my secret place. And I saw Mr. William Bennett on the road."

"Oh my! He lives right here in Middleborough."

"He looked straight at me, but he didn't recognize me."

"Oh, Debbie! Oh my! Where are the clothes? The men's clothes?"

"Right here, under the bed." Deborah pulled out a package from under the bed and unwrapped it.

"You are so clever, Debbie. You kept it a secret from me," said Jennie.

"We aren't working in the same house all the time. This is

the first time we have worked together for months. I couldn't tell you before this."

"I know. First you go there, then you go here. But I always like it when we are working at the same house."

"So do I. And then another time I wore the suit to Plympton. I talked to people, with soldiers who were going to join the troops. Not all of them enlist for a long time. Six months, or three months perhaps, though now they want men to enlist for three years or the duration of the war."

"It's a nice suit, but a bit worn," Jennie said. "Didn't anyone know you were a girl?"

"No one. I suppose that is because I am rather big, and kind of straight up and down, and thicker in the waist than a lot of girls."

"But your bosom?"

"I tied a band of linen tightly around me. I think I will make a tight-fitting undervest. I really do look like a man when I'm in men's clothes. I am not such a pretty girl. Plain, I think. But I do make a handsome boy. I tied my hair back."

"And nobody . . ."

"Nobody. But the biggest test of all was when I spoke to my mother. I was with two men going home from the army. We stopped at the house where my mother works in Plympton. We chopped some wood and carried it to the shed. She gave us some food. And she didn't know who I was."

"Where did you get the men's clothes?" Jennie asked.

"I borrowed them. They are Sam Leonard's. I took them the last time I was here. He is away at war, and no one will miss them. Anyway he has outgrown them. And I aim to put them on again and go out into the streets."

"When?"

"Tonight."

"Tonight? Where will you go? I'd be scared."

"To the inn. There is a fortune-teller there and I'd give anything to know what my fortune is. This is prayer meeting night and the Leonards will be away from home."

"Isn't it against the law to wear men's clothes?" Jennie asked timidly.

"I don't know," Deborah replied. "I don't care. I'm going to do it anyway."

The two girls helped prepare and serve supper. As soon as Mr. Leonard and his family left for the meetinghouse, Deborah ran for the attic room she shared with Jennie. "Come on," she said. "You'll be surprised when you see me."

Jennie followed her up the stairs. Once inside the room and the door shut, Deborah shed her girl's clothing and began to pull on the men's breeches.

"Aren't you scared, Debbie?" Jennie asked.

"No. Come on. Give me the jacket."

"Suppose the Leonards come back before you do?"

"They won't. The minister can pray for over an hour, easy. Then there are the psalms and everything. If the Leonards beat me home, I'll climb up the tree, get on the back porch, and come in the window and up the stairs."

Deborah pulled her belt tight and ran her hands down her chest. "How do I look?" She stood straight and turned slowly around as she put on the hat. Her hair was tied in a short queue.

Jennie drew back. Her eyes ran over her friend's figure. "You look—like—a boy!" she exclaimed. "A good-looking boy. The girls will all be after you," she added with a giggle.

"There's no time to waste," said Deborah. "Come on." She rushed down the narrow hall and took the back stairs, with Jennie following. She paused for a moment on the wide stone at the kitchen door.

"I won't be able to breathe until you come back," said Jennie.

"You will be holding your breath for a long time then," said Deborah. "Be sure the window in the back is left open." Then she turned and melted into the darkness.

Deborah walked rapidly. Soon she was at the inn. Many of the people she would see there would know Deborah Sampson. But she didn't feel like Deborah Sampson. She felt like another person, free, without skirts slapping against her legs.

She pushed the door open. Light from a few candles and the open fire made the room seem brilliant.

Fearful that someone might recognize her, she sank into a chair at an empty table. Soon Master Sproat's nephew Bob came to her. "Have anything?" he asked.

"Ale," she said, looking squarely into the face of a boy she had known most of her life.

Bob soon returned with the ale. She put a coin on the table. "I am told there is a fortune-teller here. Where is he?"

"There," said Bob, jabbing his thumb toward the corner of the room.

She picked up her mug and sauntered to the corner table. A man was seated there. He looked up. He was roughly dressed and wore a grizzled growth of beard. The second finger of his right hand was missing.

"You tell fortunes?" she asked.

"That I do," he said. "I am the seventh son of a seventh son."

"Can you tell mine?"

"If you have one, I can. Turn around."

Deborah did as he commanded, glad she didn't have bulging hips as many girls did, and hoping she really did appear to have a manly chest.

She apparently passed his examination. "Sit down," he said. "Let me see your hands."

She held them out and watched as he examined them closely. He noticed that her index finger on her right hand was stiff. "Had a felon, did you?" he asked.

"Yes. My finger was badly infected more than half a dozen

years ago. It's been stiff ever since," Deborah told him.

The fortune-teller nodded. "I had one too. That's how I lost my finger. I'd rather have it back, stiff, like yours, though. Done a lot of work, hey?"

Deborah agreed. A young lifetime of work on the farm showed in her hands.

He lifted his eyes and looked into her face. It was a hard, penetrating gaze. She was glad she wasn't pretty.

"I see in you a bright and honest young gentleman. You have a great desire for uncommon enterprises. Why have you held back so long?"

"Have I?" She answered his question with a question.

"You know you have. You will succeed in the adventures you want so much. And I do see much adventure for you. Be certain your desires are right, and then follow them. Use the strength you have. Face your enemy. Face the future bravely. You can overcome. You are young and strong. You are able to do all those things you want to do."

Chapter 5
BOUNTY MONEY RETURNED

IN SPARE moments and after regular hours of spinning, Deborah fashioned a suit of men's clothing for herself. She returned Sam Leonard's clothes, replacing them when she was again working at the Leonard home.

Dressed as a young man, she began making excursions into towns that were new to her. She was still working in Middleborough, Plympton, Plymouth, and other nearby villages, changing places of employment often. Disguised as a man, she ventured into new places, and met and talked with young men who had seen fighting with militia units.

Deborah's long absences, her vague explanations, and her outspoken words of restlessness and dissatisfaction began to distress the Thomases, and also her mother.

"You are twenty years old, Deborah," her mother said.

"I know I am."

"You should be married."

"Married?" Deborah cried. "I don't dream of it." Her mother had often raised the subject. It was one of the reasons Deborah didn't visit her more often.

"But marriage would do away with your feeling of restlessness. Young Hezekiah Brown of Plymouth is all eyes for you. He has spoken to me and would like to marry you."

"He drinks too much and thinks only of himself," Deborah said.

"Marriage will steady him too," her mother said. "His father is quite well fixed. A merchant with a growing business. He would provide you with a good home and a secure future," Mistress Sampson added.

Deborah wanted to be free from the talk of marriage. But she couldn't escape it. Her friends, the Thomases, urged marriage upon her too.

The militia musters went on, the alarms calling men to arms continued. Deborah saw each one with envy, ache, and yearning. The whole world seemed in motion, but she, Deborah Sampson, was not.

One day when she was at the secret place in the grove at Barden's Hill, she heard the rattle and roll of drums, the biting cry of the fifes. They were recruiting in Middleborough. She had seen the recruiting officer come to the village that afternoon.

The sun was close to setting. It would be dark soon. Suddenly she stood up. A new resolution came to her. She slipped out of her woman's clothing and put on the man's suit she had made and, as the day changed into night, Deborah Sampson seemed to change from a woman to a man.

When Deborah entered the recruiting house she went straight to the recruiting officer. "I want to sign up," she said.

"Very well, young man. Your country needs you," he said as he dipped his quill deep into the bottle of ink before him. "What is your name?"

"Timothy Thayer," she said.

"Age?"

"Sixteen," she replied, thinking of her beardless face. She knew that boys younger than that enlisted and no one seemed to doubt them.

He went through the other questions and handed the quill to her. "Sign here," he said, pointing.

She took the quill and began to write her new name.

"Look at that, will you? That young man holds his pen exactly like Deborah Sampson does."

Her blood froze. Her hand, and then her whole body, stiffened. She had been discovered! Her index finger did not grip the pen. It stuck out as though it were pointing at what she had already written.

She looked up. In the shadows of the candle-lit room she saw old Mistress Woods. The old woman peered at Deborah intently. "Young man, you hold a pen just like Deborah Samp-

son does," she repeated. "She taught some of my grandchildren in the school," Mistress Woods said.

"That's your trigger finger," the recruiting officer said.

"I shoot with my middle finger," Deborah said quickly. "I can handle a gun."

The man looked a bit doubtful, but said, "You will be mustered into the Continental Army in the course of a week or fortnight, with the next group. Here's your bounty money." He counted out the money in Continental currency which was due a soldier enlisting in the army.

Deborah stuffed it in her pocket and swaggered from the room as manfully as she could manage.

The passing days were pure anguish to Deborah. Why had she been so hasty? How could she ever have thought she could go to war with Middleborough men? She couldn't possibly expect to attend the muster on the green of her own home town. Everyone would be there, and would be looking at her. Then, there was the talk before and after the muster. Everyone would want to know more about Timothy Thayer, and she could never answer all the questions.

She turned down an offer to spin at the Morton's, and spent her time at Deacon Thomas's house. Mistress Thomas was glad to have her, and did not notice that Deborah was worried.

Muster day came. Deborah's mind was heavy. Again she had sought refuge in her special place. The noise had faded. The sound of fifes and drums was gone. Now she could only hear the songs of birds. She couldn't make up her mind what to do.

She heard a rustle back of the hemlocks. She looked up, frightened. Jennie pushed her way through the low-hanging branches. "Here you are," she said. "I've been looking everywhere for you. Debbie, there is big trouble!"

"What is it?"

"A man named Timothy Thayer didn't show up for the muster. They are looking for him. He got his bounty money. Then they remembered that old Mistress Woods thought of you because he held his quill the same way you do. They started looking for you. I figured you might be here. Did *you* enlist?"

Deborah's mounting heartbeats suddenly calmed down, and she knew what she must do. "Jennie, will you do something for me?" she asked.

" 'Course I will, Deb."

She pulled the bounty money from her pocket. "Here. Give this to the recruiting officer. Tell him it is from Timothy Thayer. Don't say anything else to anyone."

"I'll have to tell someone."

"No. Not anything. Not to anyone. Promise? Just say a young man who said he was Timothy Thayer gave you the money to return. You don't know anything about him."

Jennie's eyes brightened. "Yes, I can say that."

"Now go quickly."

"What are you going to do?"

"I have my necessaries, all the things I need, right here." She pointed to a small bag.

"But what are you going to do?" Jennie insisted.

"I am going to do what I must do," Deborah said quietly.

Chapter 6

A YOUNG SOLDIER

DEBORAH STARTED off on the road east, to Plymouth, ten miles distant. She thought of stopping off at Plympton to bid her mother good-bye. But she decided she couldn't do that. Her mother would never understand her being in a man's clothes.

At Plymouth she paused at the place where the Pilgrims first stepped ashore in the New World. Her ancestors had become leaders in the Massachusetts Colony. They had sought refuge in America, and now, over a century and a half later, she was seeking a new life, searching for a way to help protect the society they had founded.

She walked along the docks and the warehouse area. A ship! She would find a ship and escape from her problems, and help her country at the same time. But not here. Not in Plymouth which was so close to home and where people might know her.

She headed south, toward Rochester and on to New Bedford, the large port of Buzzards Bay, stopping at an inn or farmhouse at night. It was close to thirty miles.

She entered the tavern. There, almost as though he had been sent for her use, was a large, red-faced, red-bearded man. He was in a uniform that loudly declared he was a ship's officer.

She stood by him, feeling small before his hugeness. "Are you a ship's officer?" she asked.

"That I am. Captain of the *Sarah*, outward bound on the first tide two days hence."

"Is there work for me on her?"

"A landlubber, hey?"

"Yes, sir."

"Aye. I need a cabin boy. Want that?"

"Yes, sir."

"Go on ahead to the ship. I'll follow. Take your necessaries with you."

Deborah had no trouble finding the ship. She talked briefly with the mate, a heavy-shouldered man who looked strong enough to manage the sails all alone.

The captain soon came. "Follow me," he said.

In the cabin he pushed some papers before her. "The ship's articles. Sign here." He pointed.

She wrote her name, trying to lower her stiff finger, although there was no one about to recognize her unusual manner of holding a quill. She smiled, happy with her new security.

"Now make me a drink. The bottles are under that cabinet. Then cook me some ham and eggs. The mate will show you to the galley and to your quarters. Be sure the eggs are fried hard. I can't stand the things when they are runny. Lots of ham. Be sure. And be quick."

As she poured the drink she wondered why he wanted it. By all signs he'd had more drink than he could use already.

On deck she found the mate. "The captain said you would show me to my quarters and to the galley."

"Put your things on the deck for now. The galley is right here." He showed her into a small, greasy, smelly room and left her there. She began to build the fire, and looked around for the things for the Captain's supper.

A huge figure appeared in the doorway. It was the mate again. "I been watchin' you, lad," he said, "and thinkin' about things."

"Yes, sir."

"And I don't think you should be on this ship."

"Why, sir?"

"The *Sarah* ain't a good ship. No. That ain't right. The Captain ain't no good. The ship is all right, but he makes it a livin' torment. I can tell you are a good lad and I don't want to see you stay here. There ain't a man in the crew who would be here if he could find another berth. If you ain't hidin' or runnin,' take my advice an' leave. If you don't, you'll come to no good and you'll suffer like the rest of us."

"But, sir, why don't—"

"Don't ask me why I stay. I have my reasons. So does every

man jack on board. If you have signed the ship's papers, don't stop nowhere until you are far gone from the smell of salt water."

There was rough intensity and yet kindness in the mate's manner. Deborah wondered what forced him to remain on a ship he was warning her of. But she took his advice.

It was a long, lonely walk, but she was back at the outskirts of Rochester before dawn, determined to go still farther away from the smell of salt water.

For almost a year Deborah moved through the wide area between Springfield and Boston, concealing her movements well. She tarried at Mr. Mann's tavern in Wrentham. She found work as a stable boy. And she visited some western towns. With men everywhere away from home in the army, a strong, willing boy could always find work.

There were quick alarms for militiamen when English ships came in sight along the coast. Twenty days military service here, thirty days there. A young man who was handy with a rifle and farm tools was always welcome.

In Medway, Captain Nathan Thayer's attention was caught by the neat, straightforward youth with the same last name. "In these days of war we can use you here in Medway," he said.

"I am thinking of the Continental Army," the girl dressed as a boy replied.

"You are too young for that. You have no sign of a beard yet."

"I am strong."

"True. Work here until you are older. If a militia alarm comes, you can shoulder a rifle."

Captain Thayer tried to find a family connection, but the boy, Timothy Thayer, was not helpful. He was an orphan, he said, lately come from England. He didn't like to talk of his past. Some great sorrow, the Captain surmised.

Timothy remained with Captain and Mistress Thayer for seven weeks. Once Mistress Thayer had to warn the handsome boy to discourage the attention of one of the village girls. "You are both too young to think of a close relationship," she declared. Both she and Timothy tried to turn the girl's thoughts in another direction. Then Deborah moved on. That was the best way.

There was always reason to pause in a town. At Holden, Deborah's eye was taken by a young man, dark and handsome. His name was David Potter. She very carefully kept her distance, content to watch him. He was aware of her only as one of the young fellows around the village.

She had reason to be glad she had been so cautious. In polite company, where she first met him, he seemed all she had ever dreamed a man should be. But she discovered that as a young man, alert for girls, he was debonair, a flattering fraud, bent on deception. With men, David Potter was coarse and vulgar

and given to overdrinking. When his militia company entered
the Continental service, David Potter deserted.

What a good thing it would be, Deborah decided, if every
woman could secretly know all sides of a man before she accepted a proposal of marriage.

The English General Cornwallis surrendered at Yorktown,
Virginia, in October, 1781. But the war did not stop. Hadn't
General Burgoyne surrendered at Saratoga in 1777? The war
didn't stop then either.

Deborah, dressed as a girl, made a few short visits to her
friends in Middleborough and her mother in Plympton. At last
she felt the time had come for her to join the army. She was
ready now. She hadn't been prepared when she enlisted as
Timothy Thayer or when she signed on the ship *Sarah*. But
she had been cautious for a long time now. She had been
learning the ways of men. Now she was ready to take the step
she had been preparing for.

She enlisted at Bellingham, Massachusetts, in May, 1782, as
part of a group of men the village of Uxbridge was required to
supply. Her enlistment was for three years or the duration of
the war.

With the bounty money in her pocket, she joined others and
marched to Worcester, fifteen miles north, where they were
mustered into the Continental Army. The name she gave was
Robert Shirtliff.

Captain Eliphalet Thorp of Dedham was the muster master. He wasted no time. The highlands of the Hudson, fifty miles from New York City, guarded the North River. This was the destination of the party of fifty soldiers from Worcester. It was over 130 miles, a hard march of ten days in cold, rainy weather over the meanest of roads.

"There is the Hudson River," the sergeant said.

It was beautiful, but Deborah with the others made for a tavern at the side of the lane. Inside, the air was heavy with smoke. Her feet felt like dead weights. Worn out from the long march, the total exhaustion she had been fighting found her. She fainted.

When she came to she saw a field of friendly faces staring down at her.

"Let him have air." The face of a woman came close. "The poor lad. Come, drink this." The woman held a mug of cold water up to Deborah's lips.

"Let's put him on a bench," a soldier said.

"We will do nothing of the kind," the woman said. "We will put him to bed with my husband. Help me. I will be up most of the night serving you all. This poor lad might just as well be in my bed."

"No. No, I will be all right," Deborah managed to say as she tried to resist.

"Nonsense. My husband sprained his ankle today and I made him go to bed. You can just as well use the other half. I'll help you with your clothes." Her hands reached for Deborah's buttoned blouse.

"No! No," Deborah cried.

"Come on. One of you men help me with this poor tired lad."

"Soldiers don't much take off their clothes when they go to sleep," one of the soldiers said.

"No, please," Deborah protested as she was propelled into the next room.

"Now, let's get those clothes off," the landlady said.

"I can do it! I can do it!" Deborah said as she pushed the woman away.

When she had left the room, Deborah took off her shoes and loosened the tightness at her waist. She looked at the landlord, who had been dosed with brandy to ease his pain. The man was snoring quietly. Deborah decided she might as well accept her unusual situation. She lay down next to the landlord, surrendered to her exhaustion, and almost immediately fell asleep.

Chapter 7

BEHIND ENEMY LINES

THE NEXT DAY, much refreshed after a sound sleep in a warm, dry room, Deborah and her group crossed the Hudson River in small boats to West Point. There they were split up and each man was assigned to a company in the Continental Army. Deborah was placed in Captain George Webb's company, Colonel William Shephard's 4th Massachusetts Regiment of General Patterson's Brigade.

Forts Clinton, Putnam, and Constitution were near. Farther south, Fort Montgomery protected Stony Point on the west bank of the Hudson. Fort Independence guarded Peekskill and Verplank's Point on the east bank. Much of this area of Westchester County was a no-man's land where troops from both sides sent out scouting and raiding parties and were on constant guard.

Uniforms were issued. The coats were blue, lined with white, and had white wings on the shoulders, white cords on the arms and pockets. Stockings, breeches, and waistcoat were white. Shoes were black.

Like the rest, Deborah was issued a cartridge box with thirty cartridges, a knapsack, and a fusee, a small light rifle with a bayonet.

Many of the men gambled, drank, and sported at the taverns or at the camp followers' tents whenever they could. Others were steady family men who had no taste for such things.

Deborah made close friends with none and kept her distance from all. When it was necessary for her to choose companions, she selected the older men, those who were quiet, steady, and reliable. For their parts, they were pleased that an attractive young man joined them. Because of her fresh complexion and her lack of a beard, they sometimes called her Molly, to tease her.

Usually, her companions called her Bobby. They accepted her for what she seemed to be—a serious soldier who was probably too young to be in the army, but who performed a soldier's duties faithfully. Robert Shirtliff asked for no favors and accepted none. When he was needed, Bobby was there, carrying his full share of the load.

But Deborah sought solitude when she could. In her quiet walks she became acquainted with an old woman and her husband who lived on the back path to Fort Constitution. She often stopped to talk with them.

"I would like to sell my civilian clothes," she said, hoping the old woman might know a market for them.

"I would buy them for my grandson if I had money," the woman said.

Suddenly Deborah had an idea. She needed a place where she might be alone once in a while to take care of her personal needs. "You wouldn't need money for them," she said.

"You need money for everything," was the answer.

"Not if I could come here once in a while and use your shed to clean up and wash my clothes. Most soldiers don't keep themselves as clean as I like to be," she explained.

"Some don't take their clothes off at all, my grandson told me," the woman said. "But goodness sakes, you are welcome to use the shed whenever you like."

"I will want to come only once or twice, perhaps three times a month."

"Once a week. Come any time, Bobby."

"You take my civilian clothes and I will feel free to do so," Deborah answered, delighted that one of her greatest problems had been solved.

Ten days after Deborah arrived at West Point, her company was assigned to scout behind the enemy lines.

After they crossed the Hudson, avoiding enemy scouting parties and pickets, they moved south through the hills and woods of lower Westchester County. This was called neutral ground, but it was a battlefield in which scouting parties of both sides probed the strong points of the other. They might meet an enemy patrol at any moment.

Making a raft of logs, they crossed the Harlem River at night. This was a stream that separated Westchester from Manhattan Island, and it was strongly held by the English.

"We got across the river all right," John Beebe whispered after they left the water and had scurried into the woods. "It's what I call a bit of luck."

"Yes," Deborah said breathlessly. "Colonel DeLancey's cowboys guard it well."

"DeLancey! Working for the British! There is a hated man. His men are mostly American Tories and they've destroyed much of Westchester," John said.

"They call them cowboys because they steal the cattle from the patriots," Deborah said.

"They steal everything."

"Some of our American soldiers steal too—just because Westchester is a battle ground and the poor people are helpless."

Deborah's company spent several days in Harlem, the upper portion of Manhattan Island, observing the movements of English troops. Some of the American soldiers were getting nervous. "How long are we going to stay?" John Beebe whispered one evening.

"Until we find out what the officers want to know," Deborah answered. "No one knows if the English will mount an attack up the Hudson."

"We would be the first killed if they did."

"Perhaps not. We could fight," said Deborah.

"Do you think we will go closer to the city?"

"We are less than eight miles now." Fear was never totally absent in these wooded hills far below the enemy lines.

The command to move came that night. They made a quick raid on an English army storehouse, set fire to it, and retreated from the blaze, again using a raft to cross the Harlem River. Then they went north through the disputed no-man's land to White Plains. There they took a place in the American lines until July 3 when the company was again sent on a scouting raid toward the south.

"We are at least close to our own lines," the man next to Deborah said as they moved quietly through the woods.

"It's the third of July. Tomorrow, if we were home, we would be shooting guns and ringing bells," another said.

Deborah stopped short. She held up her hand for silence. "We may be firing guns here," she whispered. She pointed toward the heavy stand of trees in front of them. "Look there! Through the trees!"

It was a troop of DeLancey's cavalry, American Tories who served England. And it was too late. The American soldiers had been seen.

Muskets barked. Deborah heard a bullet splat against a tree above her head. Another tore off a small branch. It dropped to the ground, touching her arm as it fell.

A bugle called and the enemy turned their horses and dashed away.

Long moments passed. Deborah could hear the horses' hoof-beats coming closer. Muskets barked again and again. The cavalry had been reinforced by Tory foot soldiers.

A bullet dug into the ground ahead of her. She heard a groan at her side. It was John Beebe. His groan fell away into a long sigh. His head moved in the dry leaves and then was still.

A command ran down the line. "Fire!"

The exchange of shots continued as fast as rifles could be loaded. It grew hot. Mosquitoes seemed to come to life in the dead leaves. The command came to fall back. Deborah and her companions retreated from tree to tree. They were greatly

outnumbered. She dropped to the ground, crawled, rose and fired, crawled again. Enemy bullets found their marks. There was a grunt, a curse, a cry. The Americans fell back slowly, firing as they went.

Deborah heard the rattle of a drum and the shrill cry of a fife, shouting and rapid gunfire. Reinforcements!

They came running, shooting as they came. Deborah saw a giant of a man. He passed close to her. She knew him. It was Colonel Ebenezer Sproat of Middleborough, the eldest son of the innkeeper. She had known him all her life.

She rose and followed him, with the others. Now Colonel DeLancey's troops were in a rout. The Americans had won the skirmish.

After they returned to White Plains, those who were able to stand were reviewed by Colonel Sproat. Deborah's company was hailed as heroes. Outnumbered, they had fought and held on in good order until help came.

Deborah stood proudly as Colonel Sproat walked down the line, greeting each man as an aide gave him the names. She grinned as he saluted her, took her hand, and said, "Your country is proud of you, Shirtliff."

Deborah's face, stained with powder, sweat, and dirt, quickly grew sober as she wondered if Colonel Sproat would recognize her. She was solemn too as she thought of her three dead comrades and the two bullets that had gone through her coat and one through her cap.

Chapter 8
A BULLET FINDS A MARK

ROBERT SHIRTLIFF and Sergeant Greene stood before Captain Webb. "So you want action, do you?" he asked.

"Yes, sir," they both replied.

"We thought that the more information we could have about Westchester and Colonel DeLancey, the better," Deborah added.

"That is true. And soldiers who want action should have it if possible."

"We don't want to be ditchdiggers, or woodcutters, or lost in idleness," Deborah said. "We can find out what the enemy is up to. The Tories—"

"You don't like the Tories, eh, Bobby?"

"No, sir. It is time for all those who were Englishmen to become Americans."

"Very well. Take a party and find out what you can. But take care. Bobby will be second in command, Jacob."

They chose twenty volunteers. After a night of hard travel, they were across the Hudson and deep into Westchester. There they lay in ambush to watch the movement of any Tory soldiers who might be bent on plunder.

"No-man's land is a good name for Westchester," Deborah whispered. "DeLancey's men pillage American farms and abuse loyal American farmers. We may be able to protect our own farmers and punish Tory soldiers."

Jacob Greene nodded his agreement.

"Look!" Deborah pointed.

"You have eyes like a hawk, Bobby," Jacob said.

"Be quiet, like a rabbit," Deborah replied.

They saw a troop of DeLancey's mounted Tory dragoons through the trees in the distance. Staying under cover, the small party of Americans followed the Tory troop. The dragoons dismounted and were joyfully received at a large residence.

"It can only be a Tory house. They probably have plenty of good American provisions they have seized," said Deborah. "Look! Two boys are leaving the back door. Come, Jonathan. We will follow them." She spoke quietly to a boy near her. He was fifteen years old and as beardless as Deborah.

"Take good care," said Jacob.

Deborah and Jonathan slipped through the woods, keeping the two boys in sight until they disappeared behind a cluster of big rocks.

"Let's wait here. They won't go far unless they go through the hill," said Deborah.

They didn't have long to wait. "Here they come," Deborah whispered.

"They are carrying something," Jonathan said.

"Food is my guess, from the looks of it."

The two boys passed out of sight. "Now we will see. Keep your firearm ready." She gripped her own rifle.

Behind the rocks they faced the opening of a cave. The entrance was blocked by a rough door which was fastened to the wall by two hasps.

"There seems to be no guard. Only this door to protect it from animals." She unfastened the hasps and they entered. Deborah stood in the darkness, waiting for her eyes to become adjusted. "There is food in here, Johnny," she said.

"I can smell it," Jonathan said.

"Here are some sacks. Load all you can carry. We have a good number of hungry men to feed back in camp."

The cave contained ham, smoked meat of all kinds, cheese, butter, vegetables, jars of honey, pickles, jelly, and other good things that might be taken from an American pantry, cellar, or smokehouse.

"What's in those bags?" asked Jacob when Deborah and Jonathan returned with their heavy loads.

"Food," she said.

A buzz of interest ran through the group. "Where did it

come from?"

"I believe it came from farmhouses of loyal Americans, and was stolen by DeLancey's cowboys," she replied. "Here it is. Come and eat."

"Ah! Smoked ham!" a soldier said.

"And cheese!"

"Oh, butter! It can make even dry army bread taste good."

Deborah spoke to Jacob. "I wish there was some way we might return all of the food to its rightful owners, but I am afraid that is impossible. Before we go back to camp, let's come here and take all in that cave with us. If we can't return it, at least we can deny it to the Tories."

For greater safety they moved back into the woods for the night. Sleep came, but there was to be no safety. In the dark, silent hours before dawn a command broke the stillness of the night.

"Halt!" The American sentinel's gun flashed. Its sharp, hard sound echoed through the woods.

A large party of DeLancey's men had stumbled upon them. The sleeping Americans awakened quickly and reached for their arms.

The Tories dismounted. After a brisk fight, they retreated. The Americans followed them. The Tories became mired in the deep mud of a shallow creek and surrendered. It was over. The gunfire stopped.

Deborah felt a warmth at her neck. She touched it. Her

hand was wet, sticky. It was blood. She felt it seep down her arm and chest. No matter. Very likely it wasn't serious.

There was another pain. In the upper part of her thigh. The leg of her breeches was sticky too. Suddenly Deborah felt faint. She staggered and almost fell to the ground.

"You are wounded," Jonathan said.

"Can you travel, Bobby?" Jacob asked. "We'll take you to a hospital."

Deborah could only think of the discovery of her sex at the hospital. "No, no," she said. "You go on. Leave me here."

But her friends lifted her into the saddle of one of the captured horses. Jonathan sat behind her to assist her and they made their way over the fields and across the streams with their prisoners.

Deborah was not the only wounded soldier. Others were carried into the barn that served as a hospital. Her wounds, like theirs, were painful, but she bore an anguish the others could not dream of, the threat of discovery. She must, by all means, avoid that.

There was a small hole torn in her breeches. It was stained with blood. She knew it was a bullet hole and tried to keep it covered with her cap.

The surgeon was a French doctor. She watched him as he treated the wounded. First he gave a stiff drink of rum. Then he washed the wound with soap and water and splashed rum on it to sterilize it. He applied a salve. When a bullet was in

the flesh, he probed for it until he was able to remove it as assistants held the patient.

Her turn came. "Ah, you are pale. You have lost much blood," the doctor said. "Are bones broken?"

"No, sir," she replied.

"This one, on the head. Is it the only wound?" he asked as he washed and bandaged it.

"Yes, sir."

"You lost so much blood. No other wound?"

"No, sir. Only on the head."

"Remove your shirt and breeches," he commanded.

"No. I am all right. Honest, I am. I will wash myself." If he should examine her further, her secret would be revealed.

He was a busy doctor, happy to see a soldier who did not malinger and imagine his wounds were more serious than they actually were. "Very well. You are a brave young man. You change your clothes. You wash. If there is another wound, you come back."

"Yes, sir," she said with a deep sigh of relief.

The doctor moved on to other patients. The interest of everyone in the room followed him. While no one was watching, Deborah picked up a box of the salve the doctor used, a small bottle of the rum, and one of the small silver instruments she had seen him use to extract bullets.

Chapter 9

AT VAN TASSEL'S HOUSE

DEBORAH KNEW she must find a place to be alone so that she could care for the wound in her leg. The blood on her breeches had dried and turned dark. But unless she remained quiet, the wound would open again.

While she hesitated, she heard someone say, "Private Richard Snow is close to death. He must have shelter and care." It was Lieutenant Barton. "A Dutchman, Van Tassel, has an attic. We can put him there. But Dick will need someone to nurse him."

"Will Van Tassel want to take him in?" asked Jacob Greene.

"He won't refuse. He wants our good opinion of him," the lieutenant said.

Deborah saw her opportunity. "I will go with him," she said.

"But, Bobby, you are wounded yourself," said Jacob.

"I know. But not badly. I can take care of Dick and nurse

my own wound," she replied. She must get away from these men.

"If you think you can handle it—"

"I can. I can," she insisted.

"Very well," the lieutenant said.

It was a rough ride in a farm cart, but a welcome one for Deborah. As soon as she and Richard Snow were settled in the garret and supplied with water and food, she resolved to attend to her needs.

The bullet was a good inch into the muscle of her thigh. She did the same things she had seen the doctor do. Soap and water and rum.

That done, she called on all her courage and inserted the surgeon's instrument into the hole in her leg. The pain was intense, far beyond any pain she had ever felt or imagined. But she had to go through with it. It seemed that every muscle, every nerve in her body, shared the acute pain. Slowly, carefully, she probed. The bullet was out.

Deborah and Katharine Van Tassel, the Dutch owner's daughter, nursed Richard Snow faithfully, but on the tenth day he died.

Deborah's wounds made good progress in healing. She discovered that the old Dutchman was a Tory who offered comfort and refreshment to DeLancey's raiders. She also learned that the farm was another storage place for goods pillaged from American farmers.

She had no wish to return to her company until her wounds were completely healed. But Katharine Van Tassel started to show a personal interest in the young American soldier. Katharine had been friendly and helpful from the first. Then, shy, coquettish glances began to come Bobby Shirtliff's way. Soon it became clear that she was trying to get close to him, to touch him. This became so insistent that Deborah knew she must leave, wounds or no wounds.

Back at camp, Deborah reported to Captain Webb. "De-Lancey's Tory dragoons use that house, sir."

"I am surprised they come so close to our lines."

"It is a good place to stage an attack or seek refuge. I have heard them come and go at all hours. In truth, I passed many nights with my loaded weapon at my side. I feared they might come up to the attic and try to take me prisoner."

"We should stop it, Bobby. Would you like to lead a party for that purpose?" the captain asked.

"Yes, sir."

"Very well. The affair is submitted to your management."

Volunteers were quickly raised. Everyone seemed eager to go on Bobby's mission. She selected thirty. After night had fallen they set out for Van Tassel's farm.

"There it is," said Deborah, pointing to the soft lights in the windows.

"What are we going to do? Rush them?"

"No. We will wait here, hoping that some of the gang of DeLancey's cowboys will come tonight for their usual revelry."

Small parties of soldiers began to arrive. "Let's rush them now, Bobby," one of the corporals said.

"Not yet. They will drink more, and their brains will become more and more addled."

Her men were restless, but Deborah held them in check until midnight. "I know the custom here. By this time there will be no guards, no sober guards, at least," she said. "First, we will take possession of their horses. Two men will take them and guard them. You, Jonathan, see to that. Then take two other men and go to prevent escape from the back door. The rest of the men will follow me. Make no noise."

The horses were moved silently. Jonathan and his men then went to the back door as planned.

Deborah opened the front door and stood in the lighted room. The soldiers at the big table leaned forward to listen to old Van Tassel whisper. "It is the wounded soldier they made me take in. He is probably here to see Katharine."

Katharine was waiting on tables. "Bobby!" she cried with delight.

"I have some friends with me," said Deborah. "Come on in, men," she called.

She stepped forward. The men followed and in an instant the room was filled with her company, guns and swords at the ready.

The attack was so unexpected and so briskly made that no
Tory arm was raised to resist.

Deborah allowed old Van Tassel and Katharine to remain
in the house. She soon found the vegetable cellar and the
smokehouse and all the produce DeLancey's men had stolen.
That she took back to camp, as a prize of war, with the captured Tory soldiers and their horses.

Chapter 10

A LETTER TO MOTHER

ANOTHER MISSION took Deborah into the high land in the area beyond Peekskill. It was a brisk day in November. Suddenly her scouting party was surprised by a band of Tories. The red-coated enemy seemed to rise from the bushes. Shots were fired.

The Americans turned to flee. They made good distance while the dragoons stopped to reload their rifles. But they were halted in their flight through the deep woods by the Croton River, swollen by recent rains. They had to swim.

Their clothes began to stiffen as the cold November air struck them. "Our clothes are freezing," someone said.

"We'll all be frozen stiff."

"Nonsense," Deborah said. "We must keep moving. The farther we go, the safer we will be. The enemy soldiers are still searching for us." Her arguments prevailed, and the small group followed her.

They walked over two miles before they came to a house. A tall, lean women opened the door.

"May we have refreshments, Madam, and rest before your fire?" Deborah asked.

The woman hesitated. "We are cold and wet," said Deborah.

After a long moment, the woman said, "Come in." The squad entered and moved gratefully toward the fire.

"Do you have food for us, Madam?"

"I will send for some. I do not have enough here." She went out the door and spoke to a black man, her servant. The man started off and the woman returned. "He will be back soon. I will get you some ale," she said as she went to the root cellar which was dug in a bank back of the house.

"I am fearful of what may happen," Deborah said to Jacob.

"What do you mean? It is warm here. We will soon have ale and food."

"That slave went toward the Croton River. Our enemy is down there looking for us. I saw no house in that direction."

"Oh, Bobby, you are imagining things," Jacob said.

"I fear not."

Deborah followed the woman to the root cellar. She was soon back, and the woman was with her. They were carrying several large bottles of ale, a cooked ham, some cheese, and a few loaves of bread.

"It is as I thought. There is plenty of food in the cellar,"

Deborah announced. "This woman has admitted she is a Tory and that she has sent her man, not for food, but to find the dragoons and tell them we are here."

"The traitor!" a soldier exclaimed.

"Let's burn her house down!" another cried.

"Oh, no! Please!" the woman begged. "Here, take the food."

"Let's take all the food she has!"

"It will serve her right. It will pay her well!"

"No," said Deborah. "Just let us leave. If we keep walking, our clothes will dry. We have this ale and food. We don't need anything more."

"Are you crazy, Bobby?"

"It is only fair. She didn't steal this food. She worked hard for it. And she is really an American, just like the rest of us. After the war, she will be one of us."

The next day Deborah was standing on the edge of the cliff overlooking the Hudson River when she heard her name. "The whole town wonders what might have become of Deborah Sampson."

She turned around. Three men had paused on the path to share the view, and one of them was Hezekiah Brown, the young man her mother had urged her to marry.

"Here is a soldier who may be able to help us," Hezekiah said as he stepped closer to her. "Is this the way to the officers' quarters?" he asked.

"I am going that way. I will guide you," she said.

"That will be accommodating of you."

She began to walk up the hill.

"What makes you think this girl, this Deborah Sampson, is here?" one of the men asked Hezekiah.

"She is filled with an intense patriotism and this is the area where most of the activity is now. Deborah's mother is worried. Her brother made a journey to Maine to look for her. She has relations there," Hezekiah said.

"There are so many places she might be."

"Indeed. I aim to talk to as many Massachusetts men from our area as I can find. Someone may have seen her."

"What is your interest in the young lady?"

Deborah slowed her place in an effort not to miss a word of the conversation.

"We were engaged to be married," Hezekiah said.

Deborah smiled. We weren't even close to that, she thought.

"There are many rumors. Some say she is dead. Some say she married, and some say she turned Tory and fled to Canada. And it is even rumored that at times she dressed in a man's clothes and indeed may be in the army."

"Strange," one of the men said.

Deborah had heard enough. She knew she could no longer put off writing to her mother. They had reached the buildings. "The officers' quarters are there," she said, pointing.

That night Deborah wrote the letter she had been unable to write for so long:

Dear Mother:

I am sorry I have not written sooner. I am sorry, too, I cannot tell you the reasons for my hasty departure.

I am in a large, well-regulated family. My work is agreeable, although it is different and more intense than it was at home. My employers demand obedience and I have learned many useful lessons, though I have many more to learn.

Do not be troubled about me as I make prudence and virtue my model as I was taught.

I pray heaven will soon send us peace and an independent nation when soldiers may return to their loving families.

Your affectionate daughter,
Deborah

Deborah was greatly relieved to have at last written her long delayed letter. She gave it to a man who was going toward Boston and who promised to deliver it.

Chapter 11
A BADGE OF DISTINCTION

WINTER WAS coming on. It was the season Deborah feared. The army would go into winter quarters at New Windsor, a few miles north of West Point. The troops had been building the winter huts. They were small and each would house eight to twelve men.

Deborah had always been quick to volunteer for any work that resulted in action in the field and that would get her away from the close confinement with other soldiers. But there could be no escape from the huts when the cold and snow of winter came. She was afraid the secret of her sex, always in jeopardy, could not be kept for long in such conditions. She grew desperate. What could she do?

One morning at reveille, Captain Mills spoke to the soldiers. "Men," he said, "General Schuyler is having trouble with Indians on the Saratoga frontier." He went on. "We have been called on to enter a campaign against the Indians who are killing American settlers in the area around the headwaters of the Hudson. Volunteers are asked for. The campaign may take most of the winter. The only thing I can promise is that we will probably see little or no mud."

"Only snow and ice," someone said.

"A real joker," another muttered.

As for Deborah, she had no doubt of what she would do. She would suffer anything to get away from the confinement of the huts. She was the first to volunteer.

They marched north on the west side of the Hudson River. Often they made twenty miles a day, seldom less than ten, depending on the weather. A hundred miles west of Fort Ticonderoga, the trail they made was through a foot of snow, with drifts three feet deep. Their path had been punctuated by burned-out cabins and the bodies of massacred settlers.

"Over there another cabin is burning," said Deborah, as they looked across a small valley from a hilltop. "We must be getting close to the Indians. The blaze is still strong."

"They will get away in the snow," said a soldier sourly.

"The going is just as hard for them as it is for us," Deborah said. "We will catch up with them."

She was right. They came upon the Indians as they were attacking another cabin. The Americans advanced, and fired. The Indians, surprised at their bloody work, emptied their guns and ran.

Deborah was in the lead of the attack. A tall savage shot at her. The ball went wild. He turned and raced away. She set out after him. It was a race, pell-mell, between trees, around bushes, skirting rocks, dodging right and left, sprinting in the open places.

Why did I ever start this? Deborah wondered. He is much larger than I am. She thought of dropping her rifle. But no. There was that short, sharp bayonet. The savage had kept his rifle. Even if unloaded, it would be a club in close combat.

Deborah's legs were heavy now. It was hard to keep going. Her lungs seemed at the bursting point. But she was gaining.

The man tripped on a root and fell, and Deborah stood over him. Her chest was heaving, fighting for more air. But her bayonet was ready.

He was unconscious. She jerked at the buckskin thong that was tied around his waist. The cord came free, and as it did so, the Indian's blouse opened. She caught a glimpse of white. Deborah reached down and tore the blouse wide open. This was no Indian. He was a white man!

She quickly bound his arms behind him. That done, she loaded her rifle and, when he came to, she marched him back to the burning cabin and her own troops.

Deborah's captive proved to be an English officer who supplied the Indians with money, whiskey, trade goods, and arms. He planned the raids and led the Indians on their barbarous attacks on the American settlers. With him a captive, the threat of further Indian attacks in the area was gone. The campaign in the north was over.

The march back to the New Windsor encampment, almost three hundred miles, brought no blood of battle. As a result of the capture of the English leader, Deborah was awarded an honorary badge of distinction, an award which had been established by General Washington.

The first warm days of spring brought a new order: All troops to the Hudson River, there to bathe.

After a winter in the huts, few of the men could deny that it was a desperately needed order. Some, Deborah included, had carefully attended to matters of sanitation and personal cleanliness regularly, despite the cold weather, but no one was excluded from the order.

Fate was kind to her. While the troops were undressing and plunging into the river, Deborah found a small pool in a brook, concealed by the new growth of spring leaves. In this hidden place she was quick to follow orders.

Robert Shirtliff, the bright young soldier, caught the eye of General Patterson. When his aide-de-camp, Major Haskell, became ill, young Shirtliff was taken into the general's entourage.

The promotion caused comment. Most of the criticism was directed at Bobby's youthful appearance.

"He is a boy who does every task asked of him," said Jacob firmly.

"But I say he is too young for his post with General Patterson," another soldier said.

"Don't talk sour grapes," Jacob replied.

"He's a stripling without a beard."

"If beards were brains, we'd have a much smarter army than we have. Bobby has always done more than his share, and you know it."

"Jacob is right. Bobby deserves all they give him."

"And a very elegant horse they have given him to ride, too," Jacob observed.

Chapter 12

THE SECRET DISCOVERED

A PART OF Robert Shirtliff's duties was to serve as waiter at General Patterson's table. An army chaplain was dining with the general.

As Deborah was serving the dessert, the chaplain said to General Patterson, "I have observed your very fine waiter. He serves in a manner not often found in the army." He looked up at Deborah. "You make an excellent waiter, young sir," he said.

Deborah blushed and said, "Thank you, sir."

"I admire your fare, but nothing more than your polite attendant. I don't think it will please him, but his total lack of beard, together with the graceful activity of a girl—"

Deborah wanted to run and hide. This parson was treading on the ground she most feared. "I am not quite sixteen yet, sir," she said.

"Bobby is a superior soldier in every way. In fact, despite

his age, Robert Shirtliff should be an officer," said the general.

"Why isn't he?" the chaplain asked.

"Why not indeed?" the general replied. He turned to Deborah. "How about that, Bobby? I can obtain a lieutenant's commission for you. Would you like that?"

This was worse than anything Deborah had ever dreamed of. She had seen the young officers' free and easy ways, their alertness for girls.

"Oh—Oh—I think not, sir," she stammered.

"Why not?"

Deborah was desperate. How could she ever escape this? "Why—why—they smoke, and drink, and carouse," she finally blurted out.

"Not all, certainly. And the army would be far better off with more officers of your habits."

"But peace is almost here. Soon we will all go home."

"We must keep an officer corps and at least a small army. You could make a career of it," the general said.

"Ah, I know," the chaplain broke in. "He has a girl at home. Someone is waiting for him."

"Yes, that's it," she said quickly. "And the young lady would not like army life."

"Too bad," General Patterson said. "But I understand."

"Thank you, sir."

"Well, think on it. In the meantime we go to Philadelphia tomorrow."

"Why?" the chaplain asked.

"Some troops have mutinied there because they have not been paid."

"Congress has little money. Most troops have not been paid regularly," the chaplain commented.

"Nevertheless, some have appeared at the doors of Congress in a bad mood. But the Congress has no power to collect taxes. That must be done by the states and they are reluctant to spend more money."

"What action will be taken against the mutineers?" the chaplain asked.

"General Washington has ordered fifteen hundred of his best and most loyal troops to Philadelphia. I will leave tomorrow. You, Bobby, will follow me with four of the officers. It is important that you ride as fast as you can."

"Yes, sir," said Deborah, happy that action was coming that should dampen talk about a promotion to lieutenant.

Deborah's journey to Philadelphia in the last days of June, 1783, made it even clearer to her that her quick rejection of a lieutenant's commission had been correct. The close intimacy with her companions was distressing to her. That she did not smoke or drink brought little comment. But the inns were small and crowded, and it was necessary to share the same room. Fortunately, whatever distress she felt did not seem to be noticed.

When Deborah and the others reached Philadelphia, the mutiny had been suppressed, although Congress had seen fit to adjourn its meetings to Princeton.

Deborah's hours were not fully occupied, so she found time to visit the important places in the city. Philadelphia was in the grip of a malignant fever. Signs of it were common: carts carrying bodies could be seen going through the streets, the active undertakers, the funerals.

The army had been afflicted with disease for all the years of the war. Sickness had dealt lightly with Deborah, but in Philadelphia she was struck suddenly and violently. With no advance symptoms, she became ill on the street. She staggered for a few steps and fell. Finally, she was loaded on a cart with others and carried to a hospital. She saw a dead man removed from a bunk and she was placed on it.

The disease affected her throat and speech. Even when conscious, she was unable to make a sound. In scattered periods of awareness she came to know that there was a nurse named Jones, the matron was Mistress Parker, and the doctor's name was Binney. They hurried about the large room trying to help the many ill and dying people.

In moments of respite from the fever Deborah was able to let it be known that she sought privacy from the horror of death that surrounded her. Matron Parker, a kindly soul, understood.

"Jones, this poor lad wants to be removed from this horrible place."

"So do I," Jones replied. "But there is no place to put him."

"There is an attic room. There would be less confusion and death there."

"They die there too," Jones said.

Matron Parker read the pleading in Deborah's sunken eyes. "Let us take him there. There is no chance of his recovery here."

Jones and the matron carried Deborah to the attic room. There were only two bunks, both occupied. After a moment's inspection, Jones said, "We won't have to fix another bed. One man is dead. The other is almost gone."

"Put the lad on these blankets. It will be better and cooler than the bunk anyway. And call the undertakers. These others must be taken away as soon as death reaches them."

Deborah faded away into unconsciousness. When she again felt life within her, three men were standing in the room with Jones. "Three dead," one of the men said.

"No, two," Jones corrected him. "Not the lad, certainly. Not yet."

"They are all three dead. And I get the shoes this time. You take the breeches and Isaac will take the shirt and the rest of the stuff."

"No, I get the shoes. I tell you this is a hard way to make a living, existing off the clothes of the dead."

"I want everything the lad there wears. They will fit my boy."

"Divide the property as you like," Jones said. "I am glad the army feeds me, even if it pays nothing." He bent over Deborah and put his fingers on her wrist. "Cold," he said sadly. "No pulse. The poor lad is gone."

Deborah's mind throbbed with desperation. She wanted to shout. No thrust of air came from her tortured throat. Her tongue felt like cold lead in her mouth, unable to form words.

"We ought to cast dice for the shoes," one of the undertakers said.

"Very well. Here are the dice. High man takes all."

Deborah could hear the click of the dice. She summoned all of her power in an attempt to cry out. All she could manage was a gurgle deep in her throat.

"What's that?" asked Jones.

"What's what?"

"That noise. It sounded like—" he said hoarsely. "That lad is still alive!"

Matron Parker bustled into the room. She bent over Deborah and took her hand. "Call Doctor Binney. Quickly!"

Deborah's awareness faded again. When she revived, Doctor Binney was at her side.

"Is he alive, doctor?" Matron Parker asked.

"I don't know," Doctor Binney replied. "I can't get a pulse.

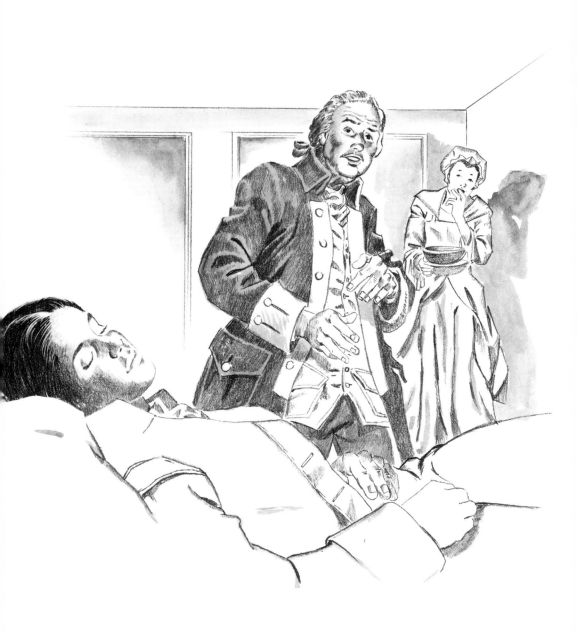

Let's see if I can find a heartbeat." He opened Deborah's shirt. "What is this? A tight inner vest. The buttons are right here in front. Let's see."

The buttons surrendered to his professional fingers. He thrust his hand to Deborah's heart.

Deborah, unable to speak, unable to move, knew that Doctor Binney shared her secret.

"Matron Parker, we must do all we can for this patient," Doctor Binney said quietly.

Chapter 13
OLD COMPANIONS SURPRISED

DEBORAH CAME out of the darkness of unconsciousness slowly. Everything her eyes found was strange.

The bed was no pallet of straw. She was aware of sheets— clean sheets. A soft summer breeze pushed gently against thin white curtains at an open window.

"Ah. You are awake. You have been a very sick person. Unconscious for several days." It was Doctor Binney.

"You have responded well to Doctor Binney's medicine," Matron Parker said. "And here you are, at my house."

Deborah's strength increased rapidly. One day Doctor Binney said, "You should try to get up today, if you are able to do so."

As she put on her clothes, freshly laundered, Deborah wondered when and how the questions concerning her sex and her army life would be raised.

A few more days at Matron Parker's house and she was well enough to be taken to Doctor Binney's residence. There young

Robert Shirtliff was entertained by the doctor's wife and two attractive daughters.

The time came to return to the highlands of the Hudson. Doctor Binney handed Deborah a letter to give to General Patterson. Matron Parker, Mistress Binney, and her two daughters warmly bid the young soldier good-bye.

Doctor Binney's leave-taking involved an embrace that would have overwhelmed most young men. He said no word about her sex, but Deborah knew he knew and that she would have to face the question sooner or later.

Doctor Binney paid for her transportation, another sign that he knew she was a girl. Other soldiers would have been expected to make their way back to camp on foot.

She rode by coach to Elizabeth Town in Jersey. The boat she took at that place sank in a storm. She saved herself by swimming to shore, but lost all her possessions except her purse with the letter from Doctor Binney to General Patterson. She felt certain the letter related to her sex and she thought for a moment of letting it, too, become lost by the shipwreck, but dismissed the notion from her mind as dishonorable.

When she reached camp, she presented herself to General Patterson.

"I can't believe it, Bobby," he said as she stood before him. "We had long since given you up for dead."

"I have been at the point of death in Philadelphia," she said.

"Are you all right now?"

"A cloud hangs over me, sir," she said. " I must deliver this letter to you from Doctor Binney."

"Excellent man. Excellent surgeon," General Patterson said as he opened the letter.

"I have every reason to agree," said Deborah as she watched the look of surprise build in the general's face while he read the letter.

She expected an explosion of anger. She heard, however, the general speak softly, thoughtfully, with a thousand unanswered questions back of his words. "Can this be so?" he said. "You have been for many months in my command, always vigilant and faithful. In many respects you have distinguished yourself. Is it true? Does your soldier's uniform conceal a female?"

"It is true, sir. I am a woman."

"But your life in the army? In the field? In battle? In the huts? The hardships? The danger? How is it possible? How?"

"Sir, it would not add to your information for me to attempt to explain. Perhaps everyone underestimates women."

"That seems evident."

"Let me suggest that you question the men I have borne arms with and shared mess and quarters with. Their answers will inform you of all you may wish to know better than I could."

"Very well. I have no reason to doubt you in any respect. But I shall make the inquiry which I am confident will only add to your stature as a soldier and as a person."

"Sir, if you will provide me with a dress and female fittings and half an hour, I will assume some modest feminine graces which will offer further evidence to you."

"Done."

Deborah retired to change. When she returned, General Patterson examined her from head to toe with obvious pleasure, but still in a disbelieving and excited state.

"Remain as you are, please." He called next door for Colonel Jackson. When the colonel entered, the general said, "Colonel Jackson, may I present Miss Deborah Sampson. She is from Massachusetts, your state, the cradle of liberty. Do you recognize her, sir?"

"I should be proud of such an acquaintance, but I have no recollection," the colonel said.

"Colonel, do you remember Robert Shirtliff?"

"Indeed I do. A gallant young man who has fallen while pursuing liberty for our nation."

"Miracles and wonders are still with us," the general said. "This young lady presents us with one of them, for she is Robert Shirtliff."

After the colonel had recovered his composure, the two officers escorted Deborah through the camp, introducing, explaining. Surprise and shock were universal.

In a few days General Patterson told her, "It is as I thought. There is no charge of any kind against your character. Only disbelief and amazement."

"Now, will you please let me see my old companions-at-arms?" Deborah asked.

"Certainly. Your old company is quartered only a short distance from here on a construction detail." the general said.

"I always looked upon you as a son," Sergeant Jacob Greene explained. "The kind of son I would like. Now I look upon you in somewhat the same light, but as a daughter."

"Me too," another added.

"But also the sort of soldier a man can rely on when the going is hard," said Jacob.

Chapter 14

A SOLDIER GOES HOME

DEBORAH RECEIVED her discharge from the army, signed by
General Henry Knox, on October 25, 1783. General Patterson and Colonel Jackson gave her written testimonials of good
service and good conduct. Two days later she set out by sloop
for New York and by packet for Providence, Rhode Island.
Given her choice of her uniform or female clothing, she chose
to travel as a soldier.

The same week Congress recognized that the need for a
large standing army no longer existed and began to furlough
soldiers. The British were preparing to withdraw from America as a treaty of peace had been signed in Paris on September
3, 1783.

Deborah was joyfully welcomed by her mother and her
many friends. But some people in her old neighborhoods of
Middleborough and Plympton felt it was wrong, even shame-

ful, for her to have dressed as a man and to have served as a soldier. Their feelings ran so high that she had been dismissed from her church. She felt it best for her to start her life again as a woman in another community.

Deborah spent the winter with her aunt and uncle in Stoughton, Massachusetts, and was made welcome in that community. There she met and fell in love with Benjamin Gannett, a respectable and industrious farmer of Sharon, a nearby town.

Her yearning for adventure had been satisfied, her duty to her country had been performed. A new feeling of maturity replaced the rebellious, unconventional notions of her youth. On April 7, 1784, Deborah and Benjamin were married at the homestead in Sharon. She discovered happiness in the life of a wife, and an even greater satisfaction as her children were born, a son and two daughters.

News of her life as a soldier followed her. To satisfy the curious she gave an exhibition of her ability as a master of the manual of arms. One of the many who saw her performance said, "She could almost make the gun talk."

Deborah responded to further demands for information about her life as a soldier by making a lecture tour through New England and New York. These activities, however, were unimportant in comparison to her life of contentment as a housewife, mother, and grandmother.

Her military service brought her a pension and, after her

death, a pension to Benjamin until he died on January 9, 1837.

Deborah Sampson Gannett, the first woman to bear arms in the United States army, died on April 29, 1827. She is buried in a cemetery near her home in Sharon, Massachusetts.

INDEX

THE AUTHOR

HAROLD W. FELTON, a lawyer by profession, is an author known for his tall tales and his biographies for young readers. A long-time interest in American folklore and history led to his first book, an anthology of legends about Paul Bunyan, and he has since written about all the major folklore characters, from Pecos Bill, John Henry, and Mike Fink to Fire-Fightin' Mose and Gib Morgan. His biographies include Jim Beckwourth, Edward Rose, Elizabeth Freeman, Nat Love, James Weldon Johnson, Ely S. Parker, and Nancy Ward.

Mr. Felton was born in the Midwest, but has long been a resident of New York City. He and his wife now have a home in Falls Village, Connecticut, where he devotes his leisure time to writing for young people.

THE ILLUSTRATOR

JOHN MARTINEZ attended the School of Visual Arts and the Art Students League in New York City, followed by three years of study in Mexico. He has worked as a display designer, done murals and portraits, technical and book illustration. He was art director for a major national association for five years before returning to free-lance work.

Mr. Martinez currently maintains a studio in Washington, D.C. He resides in Leonardtown, Maryland, with his wife and daughter, and spends his spare time painting.

j973.3
F   Felton, Harold W.

         Deborah Sampson...

4-29 25   66-9364
11-1456
1.2
5

Deborah Sampson,
Soldier of the Revolution

DATE	ISSUED TO
5-26-05	Samantha Millard